the SMURFS™

MEET THE SMURFS!

Popcorn
ELT
Readers

New Words

joke

He likes to **joke**.

machine

These are **machines**.

leader

She's the **leader**!

make magic

She can **make magic**.

2

play music

They like to **play music**.

vegetable garden

This is a **vegetable garden**. There are a lot of **vegetables**.

poem

Your hair is yellow,
Your eyes are blue,
Smurfette, Smurfette,
I Love you!

This is a **poem**.

work

5 × 5 =

She is a teacher. She **works** in a school.

Where's the popcorn?
Look in your book.
Can you find it?

the SMURFS™

MEET THE SMURFS!

There are a lot of Smurfs!
They live in Smurf Village.

The Smurfs are blue. They are very small.
They speak Smurf!

Smurf, smurfy smurf.

This is Papa Smurf. He is the **leader**.
He is very old.

He **works** here. He can **make magic**!

This is Grouchy Smurf. He is never happy!

Jokey Smurf is always happy!
He likes to laugh and **joke**.

All the Smurfs love Smurfette.

Poet Smurf is Smurfette's good friend.
He writes **poems** for her.

Harmony Smurf loves to **play music**.
But his **music** is very bad!

'Stop!' say the Smurfs. 'Go away!'

Handy Smurf loves to **work**. He makes **machines**.

He is always thinking.

Farmer Smurf **works** in his **vegetable garden**. He does not talk much.

All the Smurfs like to eat his **vegetables**!

Gargamel does not like the Smurfs. He **makes** bad **magic**.

Azrael is his cat.

He wants to eat the Smurfs!

THE END

After you read

1 Complete the sentences.

a) Papa Smurf   **i)** is Poet Smurf's good friend.

b) Jokey Smurf   **ii)** makes bad magic.

c) Smurfette   **iii)** is very old.

d) Farmer Smurf   **iv)** likes to laugh.

e) Gargamel   **v)** does not talk much.

2 Do the Smurf wordsearch.

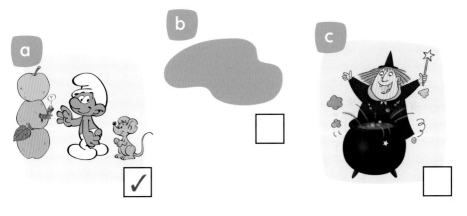

b	l	u	e	n	s
q	s	e	o	r	n
l	m	a	g	i	c
p	a	p	a	r	i
t	l	g	t	j	b
r	l	w	o	r	k

5 × 5
=

3 Complete the sentences.

is ~~live~~ wants
works makes

a) The Smurfs   live   in Smurf Village.

b) Papa Smurf .... the leader.

c) Handy Smurf .... machines.

d) Farmer Smurf .... in his vegetable garden.

e) Azrael .... to eat the Smurf.

4 Which Smurf do you like? Draw your favourite Smurf.

I like ....

because he / she ....

....

....

....

22

Quiz time!

Read the sentences. Answer Yes or No.

		Yes	No
1)	The Smurfs are yellow.	☐	☐
2)	Harmony Smurf's music is very good.	☐	☐
3)	Handy Smurf loves to work.	☐	☐
4)	Gargamel makes good magic.	☐	☐
5)	Jokey Smurf likes to laugh.	☐	☐

SCORES

How many of your answers are correct?

0–2: Read the book again! Can you answer the questions now?

3–4: Good work! The Smurfs like you!

5: Wow! Are you a Smurf?!

BA. 12/14

1 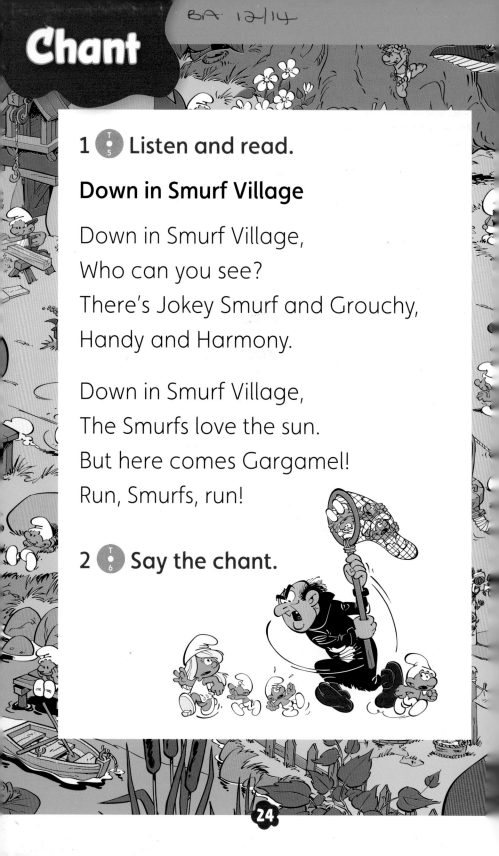 **Listen and read.**

Down in Smurf Village

Down in Smurf Village,
Who can you see?
There's Jokey Smurf and Grouchy,
Handy and Harmony.

Down in Smurf Village,
The Smurfs love the sun.
But here comes Gargamel!
Run, Smurfs, run!

2 **Say the chant.**